Spike Press

The Keys

Sally McKeown

copyright Spike Press
1989

k28·6/2321574

The Clarion

DEBBIE from Birmingham,blonde seeks companionshipBOX679
SALE Pine cabinet,table,4 chairs £180 ono Tel765234
FORD CAPRI spares offers Tel 896532
CURTAINS blinds for all your requirements try PTB Blinds Tel 745196

MACLAREN double buggy and carrycot 90 2 way baby alarm babywalker Dropside cot and mattress £80 Tel 587324
FRUIT machine £65 ice skates £12 Tel 989812
BOOKSHELVES folding as new £20 each Tel 657 897867

LOST-Bunch of keys,Allen Lane
or Trinity Common area
Phone 304727

PINE coffee table,pine Pembroke kitchen table,pine desk with leather top Offers 0546 876243
GREAT reductions on repro furniture Bales Queen Victoria Road

THREE PIECE suite floral pattern good condition offers can deliver Tel after 6 984325
TREE FELLING For a free estimate tel 695674

"Now you've been here six months,"
said Mr Grant,
"I think you can look after the keys
when I'm away."

Mr Grant is my boss.
He owns the butchers
on Stanton Road.
I work there.

He's a bit fussy about some things
but he's not a bad boss.

In July he goes away for a week
and shuts the shop.
He gets one of us to go in every day
to see it's all OK.

This time he'd asked me
to keep an eye on things.
I didn't want to let him down.

After work I went to see
my mate Paul.
He's mad about boats.

He was going down the canal
that night to see a boat.
I said I'd go too.

Do you know Allen Lane?
It's the road at the end
of the common by the canal.

There's a really good pub there.
It's called the Rose.

We went for a drink there.
Then we had another... and another.
It was dark when we came out.

"Let's go this way," said Paul.
"There's a short cut
up to the main road."

We got lost and ended up
going back across the common.

Next day I looked for the keys.
I looked everywhere.
I still can't find them.

Like I said,
Mr Grant's not a bad boss
but I don't want to have to tell him
I've lost the keys.

So if you're near Allen Lane
or Trinity Common
keep an eye out for them.

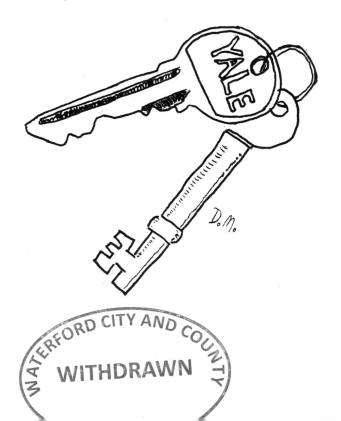